Name: _____

Form: _____

AF172850

Puberty, Reproduction & Birth

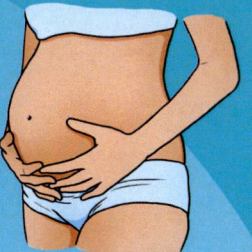

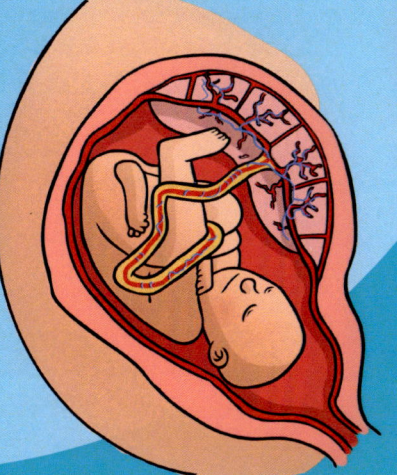

- Read, engage and learn!
- Full colour, illustrated Topic Booklet.
- Glossary, Memory Map, Active Learning Game & Flashcards.
- Ideal for Common Entrance and KS3 pupils.

This Oaka™ Books Write Your Own Notes Booklet goes hand in hand with the Active Learning Pack on this topic. The pack includes a Topic Booklet, an Active Learning Game and Question & Answer Flashcards.

Fresh Focus on Learning

Oaka BOOKS

Puberty, Reproduction & Birth Glossary

Acne (ak-nee): ....
....
....
....

Adulthood: ....
....
....
....

Afterbirth: ....
....
....
....

Birth: ....
....
....
....

Breasts: ....
....
....
....

Cervix: ....
....
....
....

Childhood: ....
....
....
....

Ejaculation: ....
....
....
....

Embryo: ....
....
....
....

Endometrium: ....
....
....
....

Epididymis: ....
....
....
....

Fallopian Tube: ....
....
....
....

Fertilisation: ....
....
....
....

Genitals: ....
....
....
....

Growth Spurt: ....
....
....
....

Hormones: ....
....
....
....

Implantation: ....
....
....
....

Menopause: ....
....
....
....

Puberty, Reproduction & Birth Glossary

Menstruation: ....
....
....
....

Oestrogen (ee-str-ow-gen): ....
....
....

Ovaries: ....
....
....
....

Penis: ....
....
....
....

Placenta (pla-sent-er): ....
....
....
....

Puberty: ....
....
....
....

Pubic Hair: ....
....
....
....

Scrotum: ....
....
....
....

Semen: ....
....
....
....

Sexual Intercourse:
....
....
....

Sperm Cell: ....
....
....
....

Testes: ....
....
....
....

Testosterone (test-oss-ter-own): ....
....
....

Umbilical Cord: ....
....
....
....

Uterus (you-ter-us): ....
....
....
....

Vagina: ....
....
....
....

Vulva: ....
....
....

Zygote: ....
....
....

1   Puberty

- During puberty, ... **and** .... **changes** start.

- This is the process of you becoming .... for sex and parenthood.

- It is the change from childhood to ....

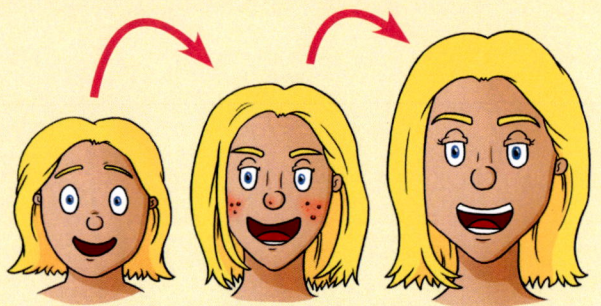

2   Hormones

- Chemicals are released from your brain.

- These .... your testes or ovaries.

- These chemicals are called ....

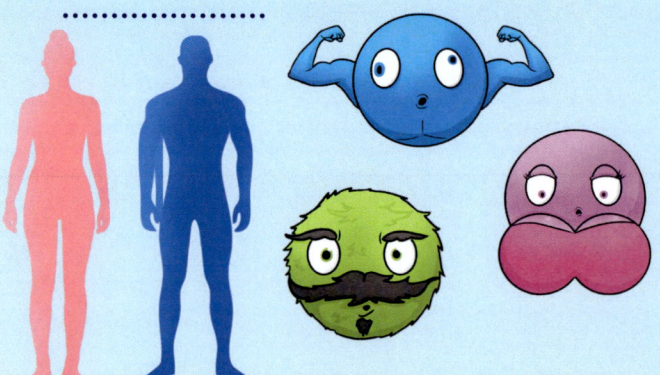

3   Testosterone

- **In boys,** .... usually starts between **12 and** .... **years old.**

- It can last up to 4 years.

- It begins when the hormone, ... is released from the testes.

....

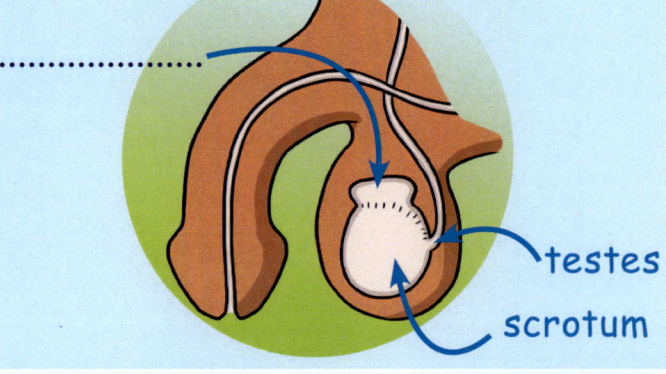

testes

scrotum

4   Oestrogen (ee-str-ow-gen)

- **In girls,** .... usually starts between .... **and 12 years old** and lasts up to 4 years.

- It starts when the hormone, ... is released from the ovaries.

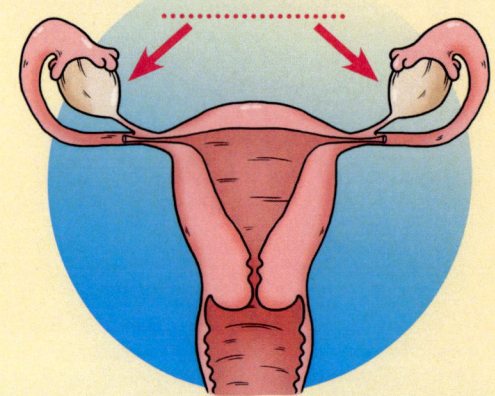

Words to help you...

lengthens　maturity　muscles　growth　testes
hair　arms　shaving　18　acne

---

5 ### Physical Changes in Boys

Part 1:

- Testes grow.
- Pubic .... grows around the gentials.

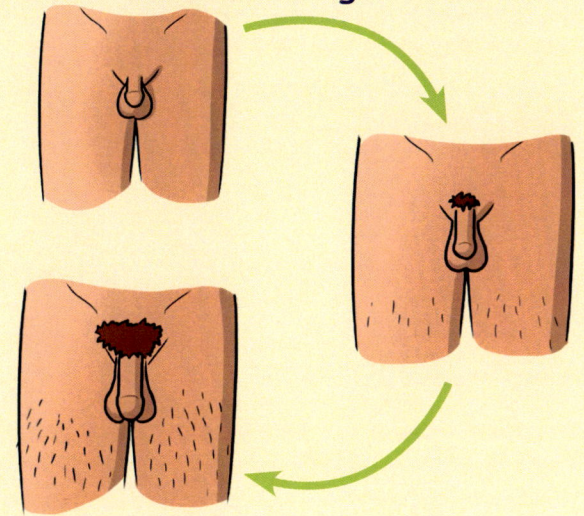

---

6 ### Physical Changes in Boys

Part 2:

- Penis ....
- Wet dreams may happen.
- Voice deepens.
- .... get bigger.
- .... spurt.

---

7 ### Physical Changes in Boys

Part 3:

- Hair under ....
- .... may develop.
- Facial .... thickens.
- Boys may have to begin ....
  their facial ....

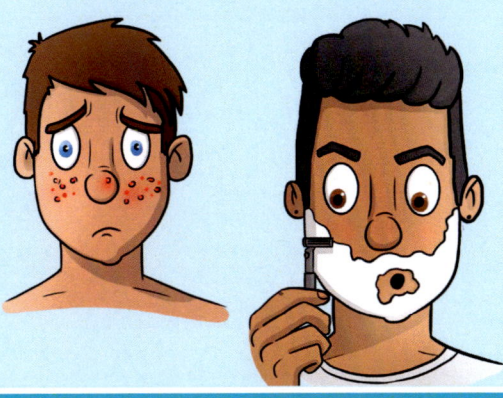

---

8 ### Physical Changes in Boys

- Most boys will have reach full adult .... by .... years of age.

9   **Physical Changes in Girls**

Part 1:

- Breasts start to grow.
- Pubic hair grows around the ....
- .... spurt.

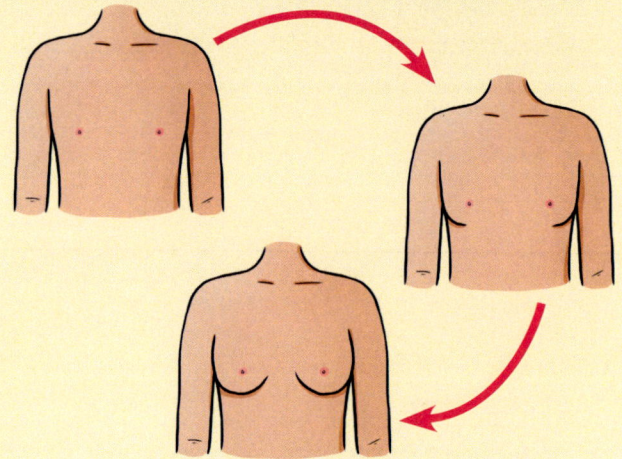

10   **Physical Changes in Girls**

Part 2:

- .... develop more.
- Hair under arms.
- ....
- Second growth spurt.

11   **Physical Changes in Girls**

Part 3:

- Eggs start to develop.
- .... widen.
- ....
  (periods) begin.

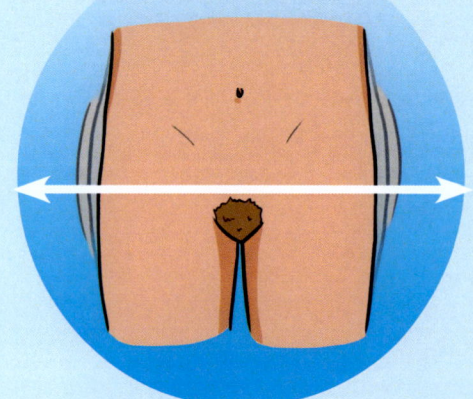

12   **Mood Swings**

- With ...., some boys and girls will get mood swings and can be ....

- Problems with parents and friends are ....

13   Responsibility

- As a young adult, you have more say in what you do.

- Laws take more .... as you mature.

- You have more personal .... for your own actions.

14   Feelings

- With physical ...., new feelings arrive too.

- These feelings can be ....

Am I Normal?

15   Attraction

- Often you become .... **to others**.

- This can be either for the opposite sex or the .... sex.

- This is ....!

16   Be Confident!

- You have the right to say .... to anything you do not want to do!

- **You should not be** .... into physical, sexual or .... acts by friends or adults.

NO means NO

4

17 You and the Law

- The **age of** .... **consent** for mixed and same sex relationships is .... **years**.

- You need to **be aware of the** .... (con-see-qu-enn-ses) (results) of your actions.

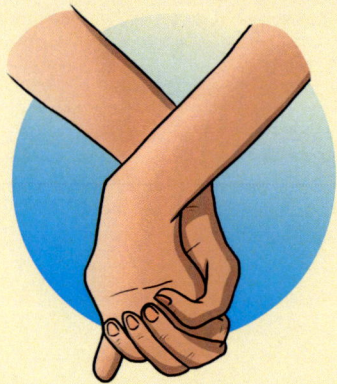

18 Advice!

- Remember that .... is not forever!

- Things do settle.

- Friendships and .... **improve** as you ....

19 Advice!

- Remember that there is a long way to go before you are a full ....!

- ...., teachers and carers all have been through it.

- They have .... to offer and an ear to listen with.

20 The Female Reproductive System

- The female .... system is a group of .... and tissues.

- They work together to carry out .... functions.

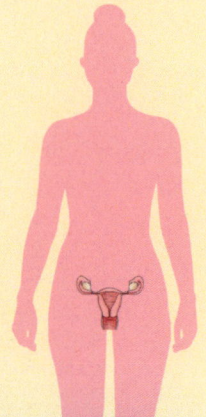

21 The Female Reproductive System

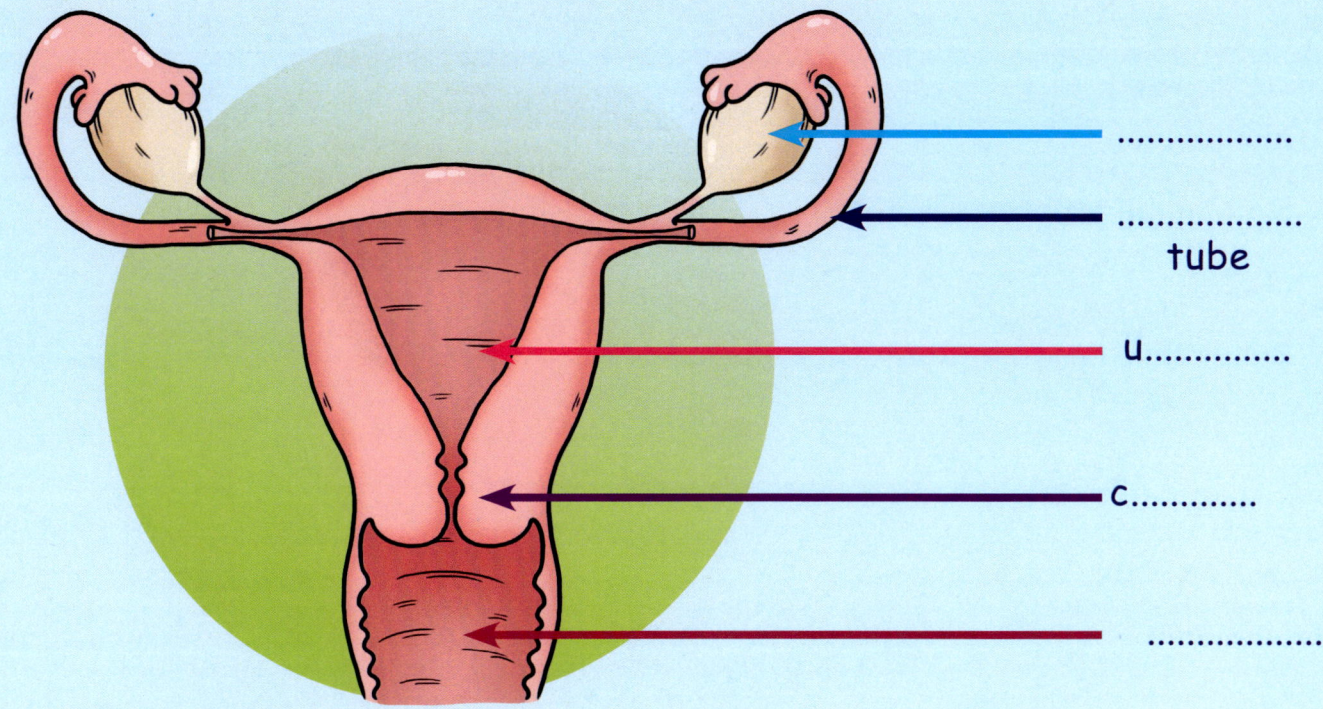

....
.... tube
u..............
c............
....

22 The Functions

The functions of the .... system are:

- Producing human .... cells.

- Providing an environment for the baby to ....

- Providing a way for the baby to be ....

23 Side View

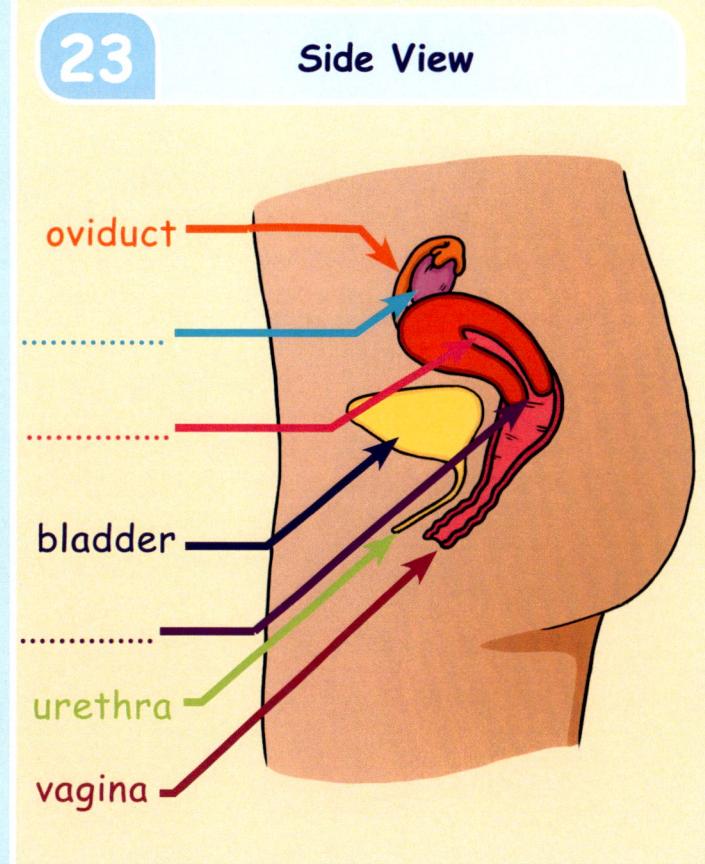

oviduct
....
....
bladder
....
urethra
vagina

6

24   Ovaries

- The .... is an organ where **individual** .... **cells grow**.

- They develop from **early** .... years to when you are about .... **years** old.

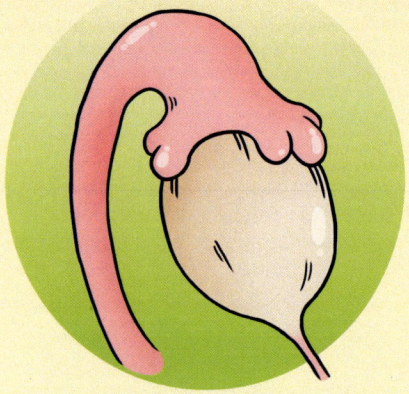

25   Oestrogen

- The ovary releases the sex hormone, ...

- It is responsible for the **start of** ....

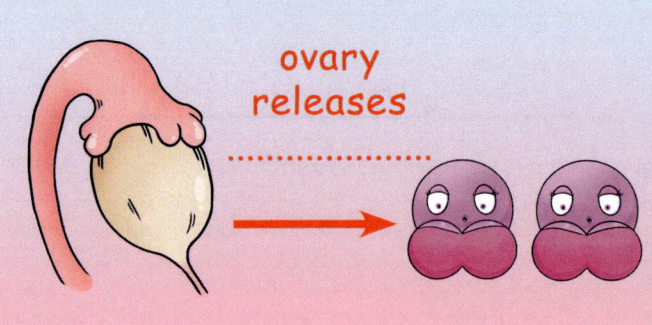

ovary
releases

26   Human Egg Cell

- A **human** .... cell is the .... **single cell** in the human body.

- It is just about visible with the naked eye.   ....
....
....

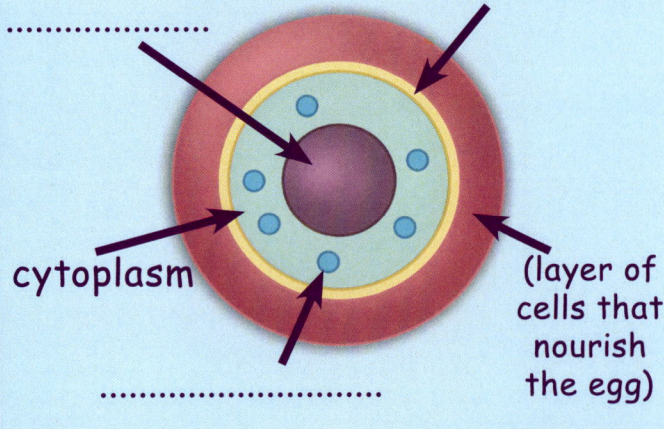

cytoplasm

(layer of cells that nourish the egg)

....

27   Human Egg Cell

- It **carries half of the** .... **information** for a baby.

- This is the .... half.

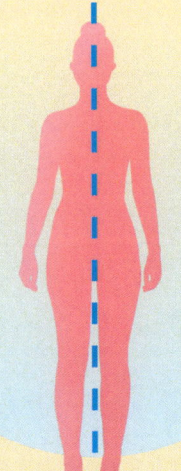

28   Fallopian Tube / Oviduct

- The .... **tube** (also known as the ....) **carries the egg** from the ovary to the ....

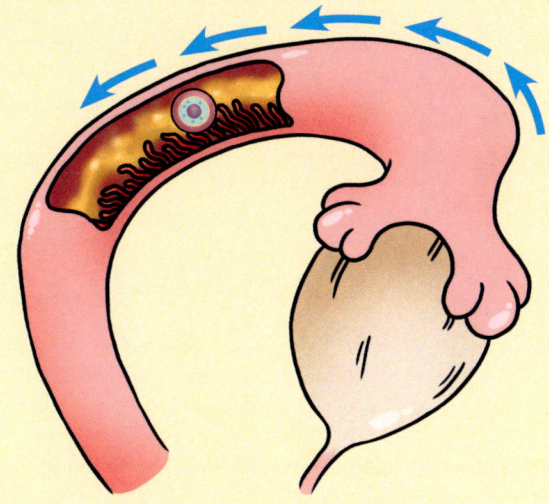

29   Fallopian Tube / Oviduct

- It is lined with specialised cells called ....

- These are ....**-like projections** which move together.

- They .... the egg from the .... towards the ....

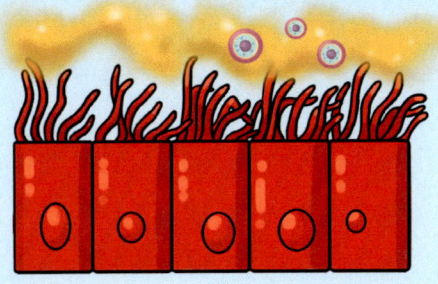

30   The Uterus

- The **uterus** is a .... organ.

- It is about the size of a ....

- It **is where a** .... develops and grows.

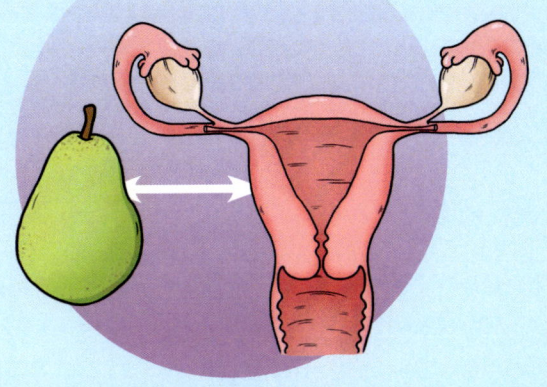

31   The Lining

- The lining of the uterus is called the ....

- Each .... the endometrium gets ready for the .... **egg** to arrive.

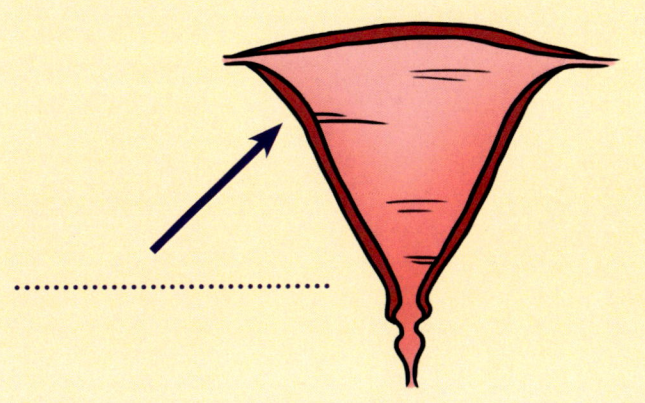

....

Words to help you...

cervix   closed   baby   contracts   uterine   vagina   penis   eggs
infections   vulva   tissue   urethra   menstruation   fertilised
contractions   genitals   relaxes   acidic   month   puberty

32 — The Cervix

- The .... is a tough cone of muscle.

- It is normally .... and helps support a growing unborn ....

- It .... **at birth**. The uterine .... push the baby through it.

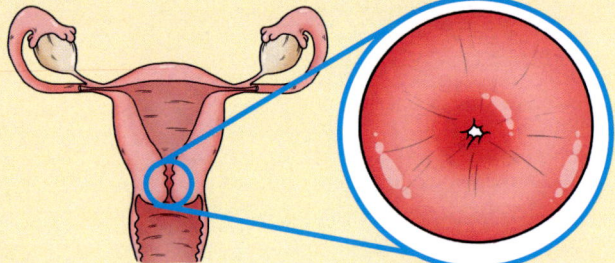

33 — The Vagina

- The .... is a muscular tube.

- This is where the .... enters during sex.

- It has has **weak** .... **secretions** to help protect against ....

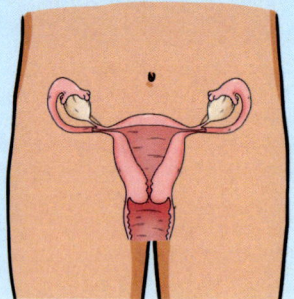

34 — The Vulva

- The .... is the **external** part of female ....

- It is **folds of** .... covering the opening of the **vagina** and .... (the tube from the bladder).

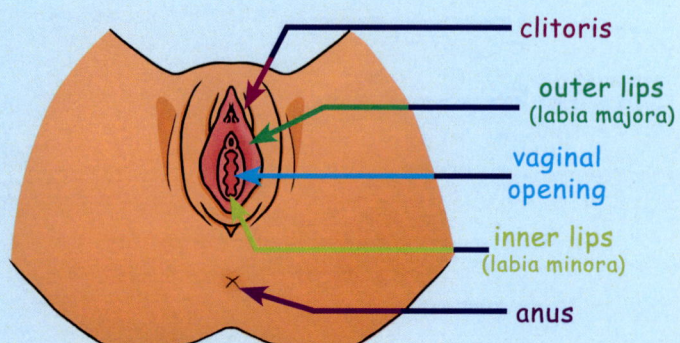

clitoris

outer lips
(labia majora)

vaginal
opening

inner lips
(labia minora)

anus

35 — Menstruation

- .... occurs **every** .... from ...., until menopause (where .... stop being released).

- If the egg is **not** ...., it will **leave the body** during menstruation.

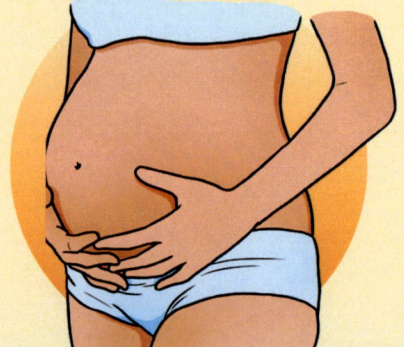

36   The Male Reproductive System

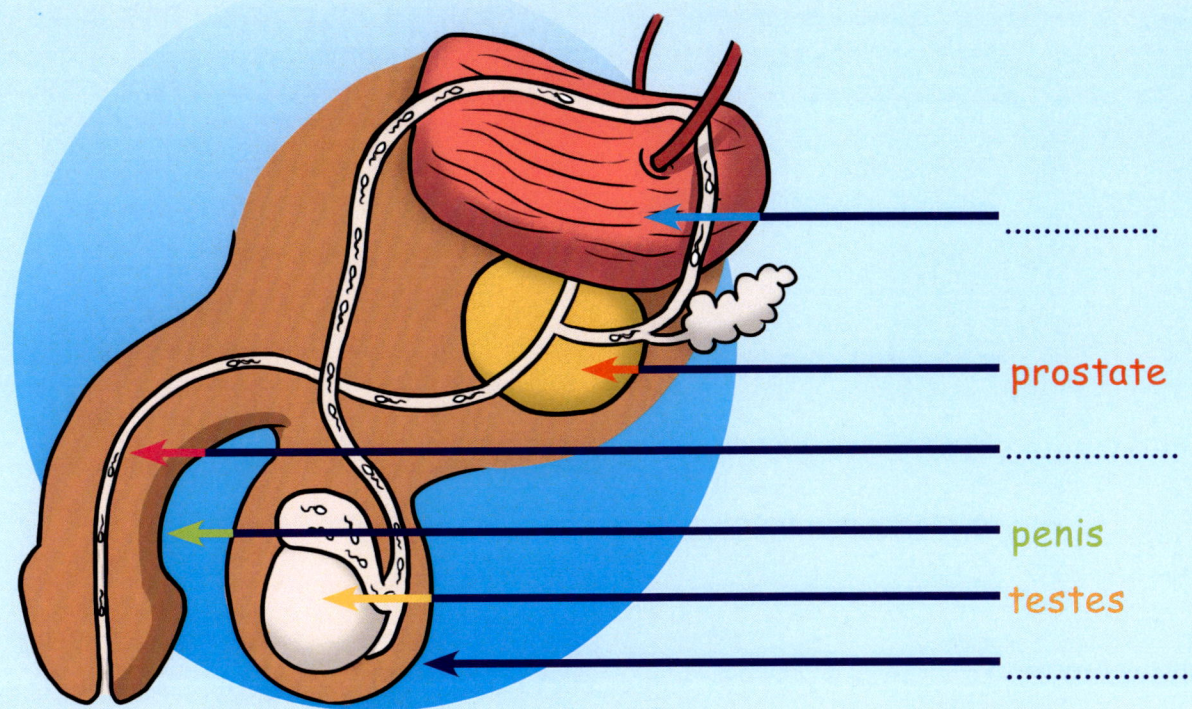

....

prostate

....

penis

testes

....

37   Testes

- The .... are found behind the penis.

- They are found in a sac of skin called the ....

- The **testes release** .... and **make** .... **cells.**

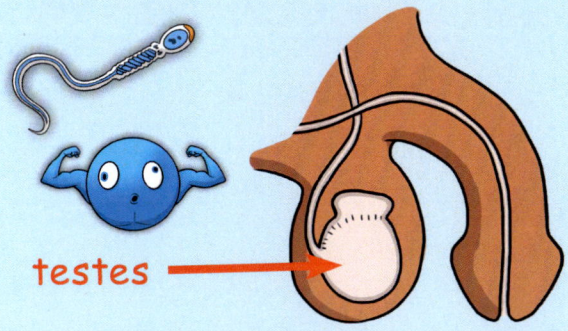

testes

38   Sperms Cells

- Sperm cells have the other **half of** .... **information** needed to create a new baby.

- This .... information comes from the ....

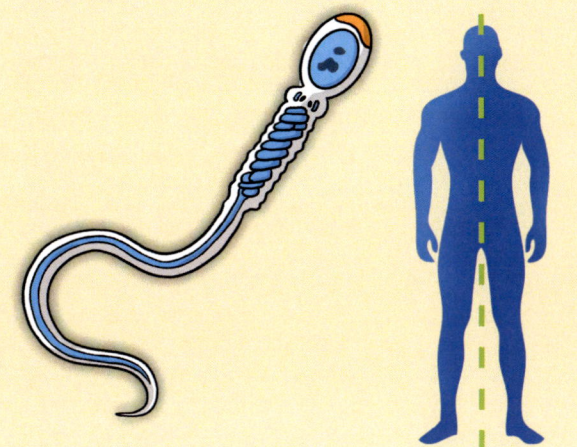

Words to help you...

sperm duct   hormones   epididymis   testes   tails
energy   seminal   ejaculation   fertilise   head   swim
100 million   chemicals   receptors   egg

39   Sperm Cells

- Sperm cells have .... to help them swim to the ....

- The mitochondria in sperm cells, releases .... to help them ....

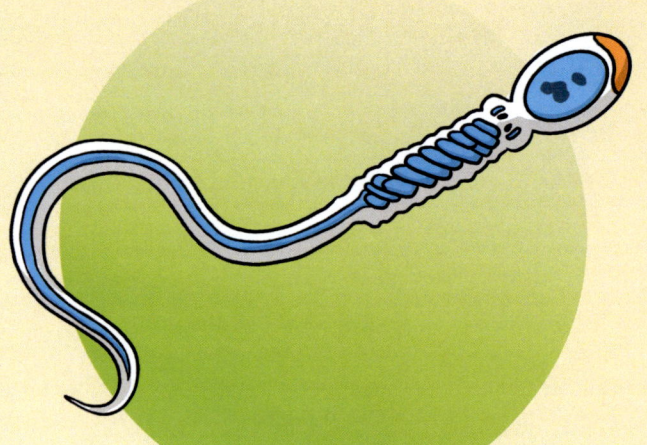

40   Head of the Sperm

- In the .... of the sperm cells, there are ....

- These find the .... within the egg.

- It also has .... that break through the wall of the egg.

- This is so it can .... the egg.

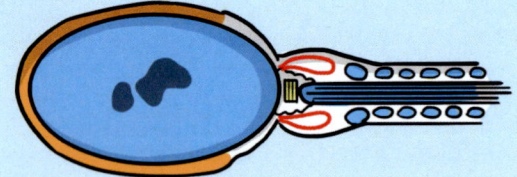

41   Ejaculation

- Over .... sperm cells are produced every day in the ....!

- These cells are stored in the ....

- There are 300 - 500 million sperm cells in one ....

42   Move On Up!

- Sperm move up the .... from the epididymis.

- Fluids are added from different glands.

- The .... vesicles add a sugary solution.

- This is an .... source for the sperm.

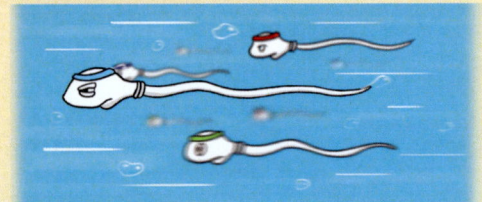

Words to help you...

bladder   erect   semen   survive   alkali   blood   acid
vagina   testes   rectum   neutralizes   arousal
cervix   ejaculated   vagina   intercourse

43   Semen

- The prostate gland adds an .... solution.

- This .... the .... in the vagina.

- This gives the sperm more chance to ....

- When the sperm and solution mix, it is called ....

44   Sexual Intercourse

- During sexual .... the tissue within the penis fills with ....

- It becomes ....

- The erect penis is put into the vagina during sexual ....

- .... is then .... into the vagina.

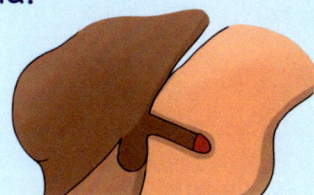

45   Sexual Intercourse

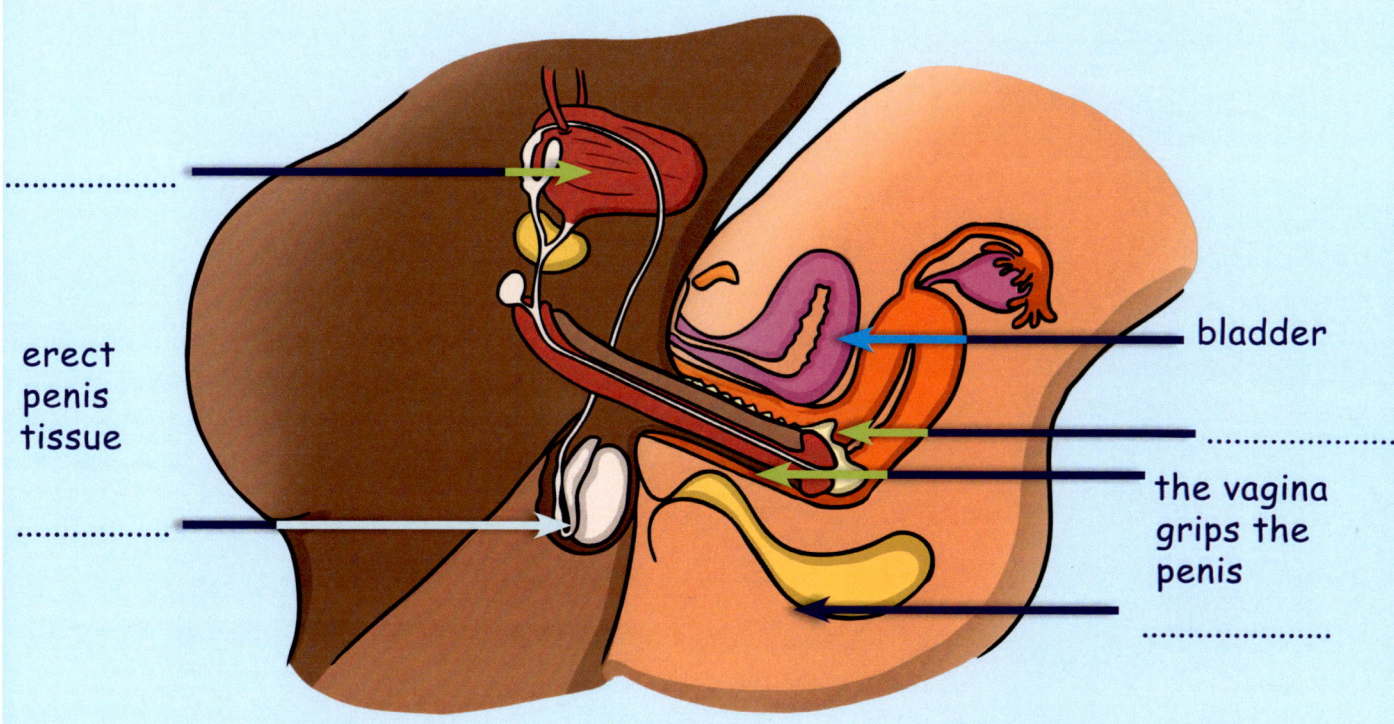

erect penis tissue

....

....

bladder

....

the vagina grips the penis

....

Words to help you...

fertilisation   fallopian   directions   cervix   sexual
blastocyst   implants   zygote   fetus   embryo   wall
swim   ovary   fallopian   egg

46   Just Keep Swimming...

- When ejaculated into the vagina, sperm cells begin to ....

- The sperm move in **random** ....

- Some pass through the .... and enter the .... tubes.

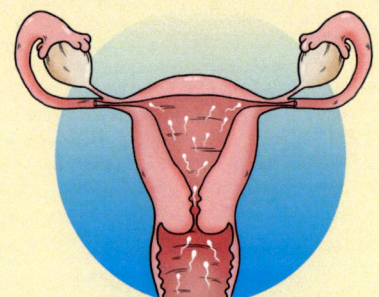

47   Fertilisation

- If an egg has been **released from an** .... during .... intercourse, ... can happen.

- .... is when a sperm cell **fuses** (joins) with a human .... cell.

- This happens in the .... **tube**.

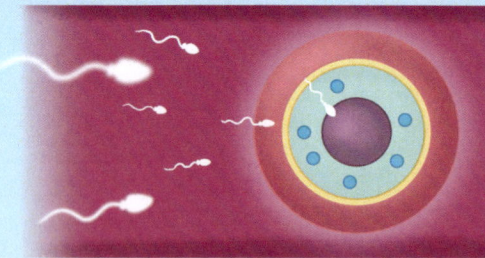

48   Zygote

- When the egg and the sperm cell fuse together, the new cell is called a ....

- The .... moves towards the **uterus**.

- As it moves, it makes a **ball of cells**. This is called a ....

49   Implantation

- When the .... reaches the uterus, it .... itself into the **uterus** ....

- This is where it **develops into** the .... and then **the** ....

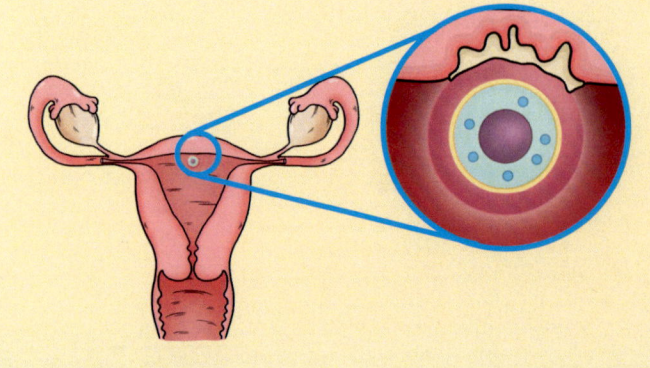

13

50   Amnion

- For **42 weeks**, the .... is carried in the ....

- A fluid-filled sac called the .... helps the baby.

- It **supports and** .... the growth of the baby.

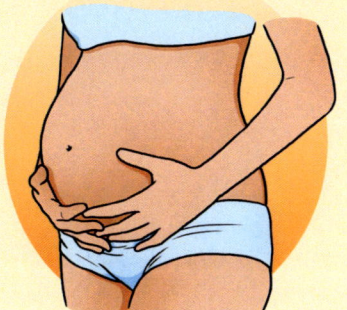

51   The Placenta

- The .... **exchanges substances** between the mother's and the unborn baby's ....

- However, their blood never ....!

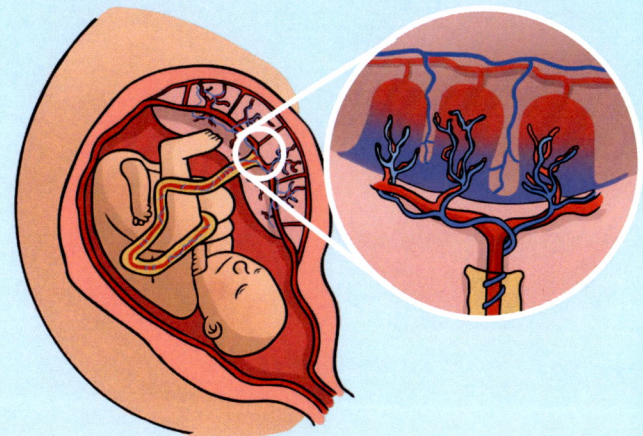

52   Nutrients and Waste!

- .... and **nutrients** are passed through the ....

- They go **into** the **baby's** .... in the placenta.

- These substances come **from** the **mother's** ....

- This helps the baby to **develop and grow**.

- **Waste** products, like ...., **leave** the baby through the **umbilical** ....

- The waste moves across into the mother's .... at the ....

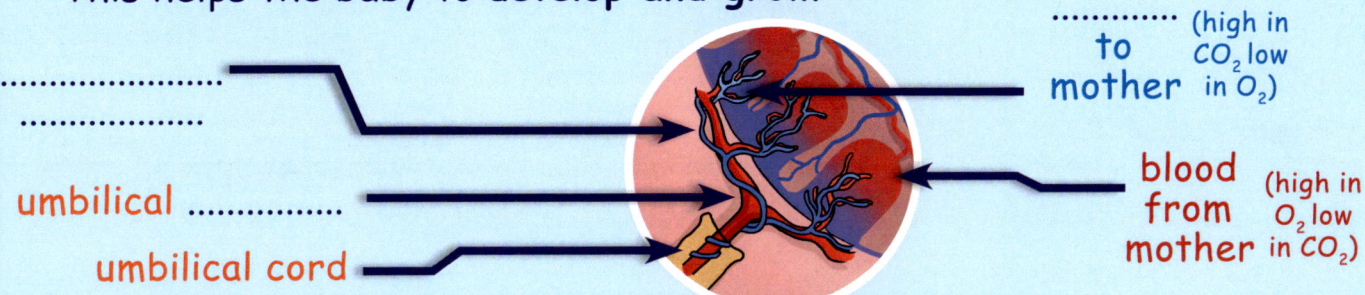

.... (high in CO_2 low in O_2)
to mother

blood from mother (high in O_2 low in CO_2)

....
....

umbilical ....

umbilical cord

14

Words to help you...

size   drugs   37   risk   smoking   head   birth   vagina
contract   grow   placenta   drinking   afterbirth   9   premature
uterus   lifestyle   diet

53 — Looking After The Unborn Baby

• ...., ... and taking .... can harm an unborn baby.

• Mothers need a healthy .... and .... for their unborn baby to ....

54 — Giving Birth

• However, babies can be born early.

• Babies born **before** .... weeks are called ....

• The earlier they are born the more at .... they are.

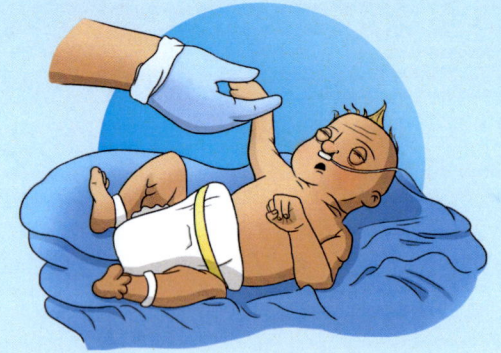

55 — Coming Out!

• Babies are usually born .... **first**!

• **Hormones** in the mother and baby **start the** ....

• The uterus begins to ....

• This pushes the baby through the ....

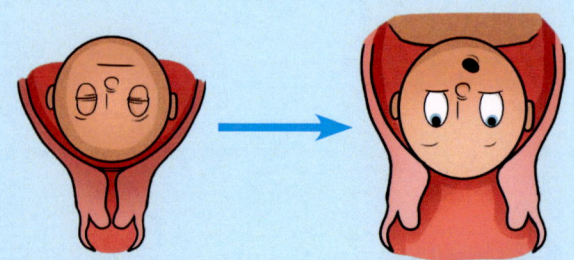

56 — The Afterbirth

• Contractions still carry on to deliver the ...., also known as ....

• The contractions help the .... to return to its normal ....

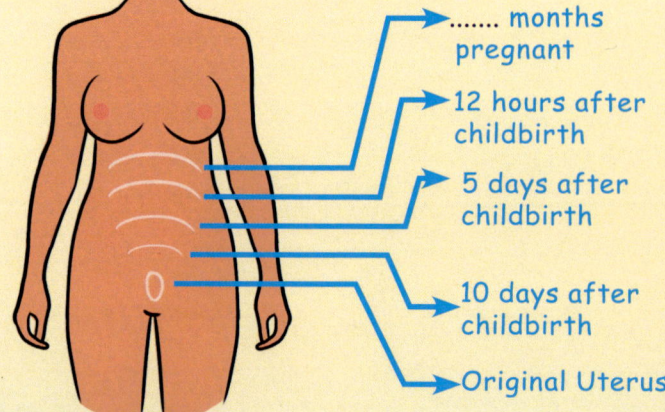

.... months pregnant

12 hours after childbirth

5 days after childbirth

10 days after childbirth

Original Uterus

Days 1 - 4

- If the egg is not ...., it will be bled out.

- This happens ....

Days 5 - 13

- The .... of the uterus lining ....

- The blood flow increases.

uterus lining thickens

MAINTENANCE IN PROGRESS

Menstrual Cycle

○ Fertile Days

○ menstruation

			1	2	3	
4	5	6	7	8	9	10
11	12	13	14	15	16	17
18	19	20	21	22	23	24
25	26	27	28			

Days 17 - 28

- .... maintain the lining of the uterus.

- This is in case an egg is ....

- After this the .... cycle goes back to day 1.

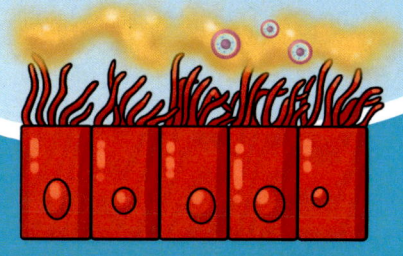

Days 14 - 17

- A .... egg is released from the ovary into the .... tube before it moves towards the uterus.

- If the woman has ...., she is likely to become .... during this time.

16

Memory Map (use this page to create your own memory map)

CE/KS3
Puberty, Reproduc-

Write Your Own Notes Booklet

ISBN 978-1-911189-55-8

ISBN 978-1-909892-75-7
Produced in association with Kate Doehren, MA Ed, B.Ed Hons, RSA Dip, Sp LD/Dyslexia
Director of Learning Support, Hurstpierpoint College